THE WORLD OF
ANDY CAPP

by
Reg Smythe

MIRROR PUBLICATIONS

INTRODUCTION

If there's anything a man hates, it's being shown up in front of his mates (see previous page).

It could have been worse, I suppose. It's been known for Flo to bring Andy his dinner to the pub and plonk it on the bar-top in front of him, knife, fork, spoon and all. Mind you, I did suspect her motive on that occasion. I think she just wanted to show off the "Hostess" trolley she'd bought in a jumble sale.

She is a bit of a nut, though, about eating dinner when it's just right.

Andy says that he likes it better when it's left in the oven and dried up a bit, like till closing time. Flo says he's just too plastered to tell the difference.

What's the big deal about Christmas dinner, anyway? Her mother will be round as usual. And probably that sanctimonious brother of hers – guaranteed to put the mockers on it. Wouldn't you think he'd feel a fool sitting there in a party hat? And if he says just one more time that the turkey tastes much better than *last* year, I think Andy will go for him. Come to that, Flo might beat him to it.

Another thing – he always insists on helping with the washing-up. No wonder his wife left him.

I've always agreed with Andy that, for a good time, it's not what's on the table, it's what's on the chairs.

Andy and Florrie wish you all the best – me, too.

Cheers,

Reg. Smythe.

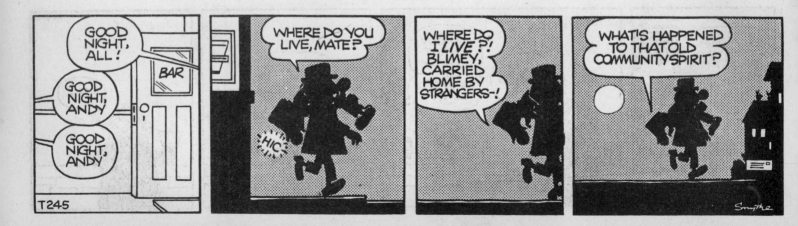

T290

T291

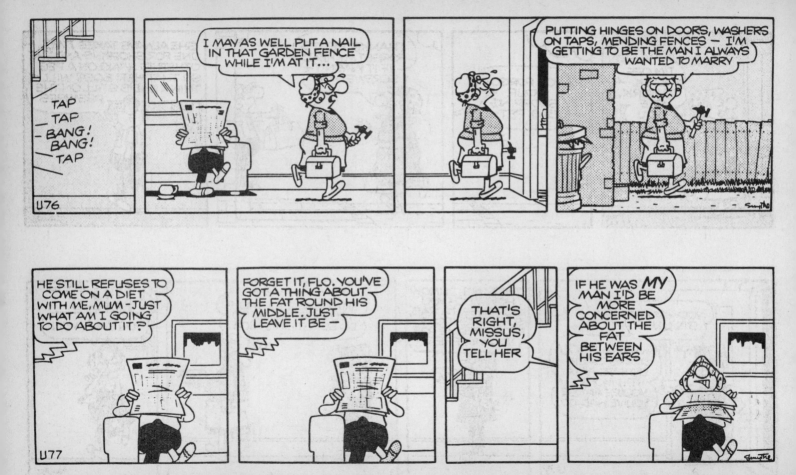

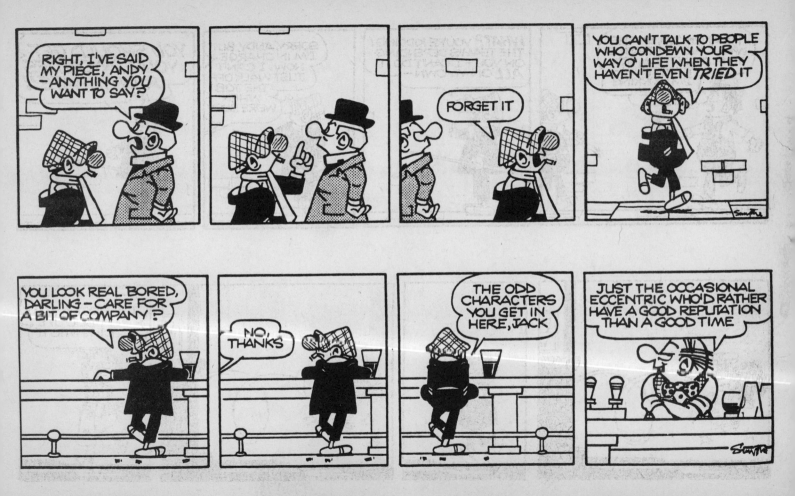

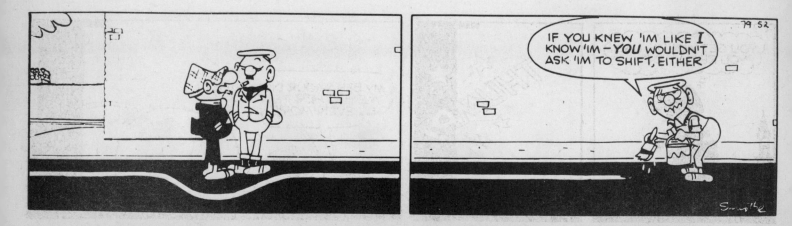

© 1986 Mirror Publications Ltd.
First published in Great Britain by Mirror Publications Ltd., Maxwell House, 74 Worship Street, London EC2A 2EN
Colour printing by Creative Print & Design, Harmondsworth, Middx. Printed in Great Britain by Spottiswoode Ballantyne Printers Ltd.,
Colchester and London. Distributed by Odhams Distribution Ltd., London. Tel: 01-831 1707
ISBN 0 85939 492 1
Advertisement Director: Steve Flaws Tel: 01-377 4901/4783
Northern Advertisement Office: John Denson Tel: 021 643 4386